Dolly P

I DON'T REGRET ANYTHING I'VE DONE.

I MAY REGRET HAVING BEEN CAUGHT DOING IT,

BUT I DON'T REGRET ANYTHING; OTHERWISE, I WOULDN'T HAVE DONE IT.

I'VE BEEN AROUND LONG ENOUGH FOR PEOPLE TO PRETTY MUCH FIGURE ME OUT. I KNOW I LOOK ARTIFICIAL, BUT I WANT PEOPLE TO KNOW I'M TOTALLY REAL.

I KNOW I LOOK PHONY, BUT I'M A COUNTRY GIRL, BORN IN LOCUST RIDGE, TENNESSEE, AT HEART. BESIDES, IT COSTS A LOT OF MONEY TO LOOK THIS CHEAP.

(FORGIVE THE CRAZY BOOTS. I'M SHORT. IN ORDER TO GET TO MY CABINETS, I'VE GOTTA WEAR MY HIGH HEELS).

A LOT OF PEOPLE HAVE SAID I'D HAVE PROBABLY DONE A LOT BETTER IN MY CAREER IF I HADN'T LOOKED SO GAUDY. I DRESS TO BE COMFORTABLE FOR ME, AND YOU SHOULDN'T BE BLAMED IF YOU WANT TO LOOK PRETTY, RIGHT?

THIS STATUE, OUTSIDE THE COUNTY COURTHOUSE IN SEVIERVILLE, TENNESSEE REMINDS ME OF MY ROOTS.

DOLLY REBECCA PARTON! DON'T STARE. IT AIN'T POLITE.

MY LOOK WAS INSPIRED BY THE TOWN TRAMP. I THOUGHT SHE WAS ABSOLUTELY BEAUTIFUL BECAUSE SHE LOOKED LIKE A MOVIE STAR TO ME.

SHE HAD THOSE PILES OF BLEACHED HAIR, RED LIPSTICK, NAILS AND CHEEKS AND HIGH HEEL SHOES. BEAUTIFUL.

BESIDES, I'D NEVER STOOP SO LOW AS TO BE FASHIONABLE.

IT'S HARD TO BE A DIAMOND IN A RHINESTONE WORLD.

I'VE ALWAYS LOVED GOOD, OL' FASHIONED COUNTRY MUSIC.

LOOK, IF YOU TALK BAD ABOUT COUNTRY MUSIC, IT'S LIKE SAYING BAD THINGS ABOUT MY MOMMA. THEM'S FIGHTIN' WORDS.

♪♪"THIBODAUX FONTAINEAUX THE PLACE IS BUZZIN'. KINFOLK COME TO SEE YVONNE BY THE DOZEN."♪♪

♪♪"DRESS IN STYLE AND GO HOG WILD - ME OH MY-"♪♪

OH! UNCLE BILLY, I DIDN'T SEE YOU THERE!

WELL, SUGAR, DON'T STOP SINGING OL' HANK ON MY ACCOUNT!

♪♪"SON OF A GUN, WE'LL HAVE BIG FUN ON THE BAYOU!"♪♪

♪♪"SON OF A GUN, WE'LL HAVE BIG FUN ON THE BAYOU!"♪♪

UNCLE BILLY SAW SOMETHING IN ME. I'M THE FOURTH OF TWELVE KIDS, AND WE WERE ALWAYS SINGING, PLAYING INSTRUMENTS... ANYTHING TO KEEP US BUSY.

BUT BILLY THOUGHT I HAD THE MAKINGS OF A STAR. A MUSICIAN IN HIS OWN RIGHT, HE INSPIRED ME TO START SINGING PROFESSIONALLY.

HE TAUGHT ME HOW TO PLAY GUITAR AND WRITE MY OWN SONGS.

HE USED TO SAY, "FIND OUT WHO YOU ARE AND DO IT ON PURPOSE!" SO I DID.

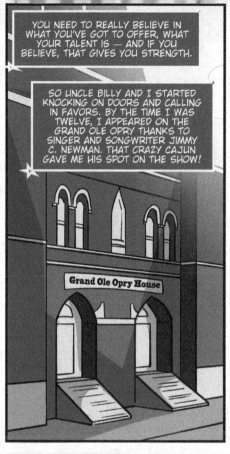

YOU NEED TO REALLY BELIEVE IN WHAT YOU'VE GOT TO OFFER, WHAT YOUR TALENT IS — AND IF YOU BELIEVE, THAT GIVES YOU STRENGTH.

SO UNCLE BILLY AND I STARTED KNOCKING ON DOORS AND CALLING IN FAVORS. BY THE TIME I WAS TWELVE, I APPEARED ON THE GRAND OLE OPRY THANKS TO SINGER AND SONGWRITER JIMMY C. NEWMAN. THAT CRAZY CAJUN GAVE ME HIS SPOT ON THE SHOW!

Grand Ole Opry House

BUT I WANTED MORE. WHEN I WAS SIXTEEN, UNCLE BILLY BROUGHT ME TO THE OFFICES OF TREE PUBLISHING.

WE'RE HERE TO SEE YOUR –

HE'S OUT.

NOW, WHO DID YOU THINK I –

YOU DON'T HAVE AN APPOINTMENT.

"FINE. WE'LL WAIT."

AND WE DID. ALL DAY. I THINK THEY FINALLY SAW US BECAUSE THEY WANTED TO CLOSE THE OFFICE.

THAT EVENING, UNCLE BILLY AND I SIGNED A DEAL WITH MERCURY RECORDS AND I RECORDED "IT MAY NOT KILL ME (BUT IT'S SURE GONNA HURT)" AND "I WASTED MY TEARS (WHEN I CRIED OVER YOU.)"

IF YOU HAVEN'T HAD THIS EXPERIENCE, LET ME TELL YA, IT'S A WARM FEELIN' TO HEAR YOUR MUSIC ON THE RADIO.

THAT'S ABOUT THE TIME I DECIDED THAT I NEEDED AN IMAGE MAKEOVER. A NEW LOOK. SOMETHING TO MAKE ME STAND OUT FROM THE CROWD.

I'M NO NATURAL BEAUTY. IF I'M GONNA HAVE ANY LOOKS AT ALL, I'M GONNA HAVE TO CREATE THEM.

I GOT TO FIXIN' MYSELF UP. I WANTED MY CLOTHES TIGHT, MY MAKEUP BRIGHT, MY NAILS LONG, MY LIPS RED.

NOWADAYS, IF I SEE SOMETHING SAGGIN', BAGGIN', OR DRAGGIN', I'LL GET IT NIPPED, TUCKED, OR SUCKED. BACK THEN I DIDN'T HAVE TWO DIMES TO RUB TOGETHER.

I GRADUATED HIGH SCHOOL WHEN I WAS EIGHTEEN. I ASKED MY RELATIVES FOR MONEY INSTEAD OF GIFTS.

THE NEXT DAY, I JUMPED ON A GREYHOUND BOUND FOR NASHVILLE. I WOULD'VE LEFT EARLIER, BUT DADDY WOULD'VE HUNTED ME DOWN WITH A SHOTGUN AND DRUG ME BACK TO SEVIER COUNTY. I JUST KNOW IT.

I ENDED UP HERE, IN A SMALL APARTMENT ABOVE THE WISHY WASHY LAUNDROMAT.

WISHY-WASHY
LAUNDR-O-MAT

ALL I HAD WERE MY DREAMS, MY OLD GUITAR, THE SONGS I HAD WRITTEN, AND THE REST OF MY BELONGINGS IN A SET OF MATCHING LUGGAGE—THREE PAPER BAGS FROM THE SAME GROCERY STORE.

YOU SAID YOU'VE DRIVEN BY A FEW TIMES. WHAT MADE YOU STOP TODAY?

WELL, I WAS GOING TO SAY SOMETHING FUNNY TO GET YOU TO LAUGH, BUT I CHANGED MY MIND.

CARL THOMAS DEAN'S NOT IN SHOW BUSINESS, AND THAT'S JUST FINE WITH ME. HE'S MORE OF A LONER.

HE DOESN'T PARTICULARLY CARE ABOUT BEING AROUND ANYBODY BUT ME.

WHAT WERE YOU GONNA SAY?

HE DIDN'T HARBOR DREAMS OF LEAVING TENNESSEE OR MAKING IT BIG SOMEHOW. HE WANTED TO RUN AN ASPHALT BUSINESS AND ENJOY HIS LIFE.

I WAS GOING TO SAY, "HEY, AREN'T YOU WORRIED ABOUT GETTIN' A SUNBURN IN THAT OUTFIT?"

WHAT MAKES HIM ATTRACTIVE IS THAT HE'S SUPPORTIVE, VERY SECURE WITHIN HIMSELF, AND NOT THE JEALOUS TYPE.

HA! THAT'S HYSTERICAL! I NEVER GAVE IT MUCH THOUGHT. I RECKON I JUST WANTED TO BE COMFORTABLE.

ABOUT MY LEGIONS OF FANS, HE SAID,

"WELL, HELL, I KNOW IT'S NOT EASY OUT THERE. I'D FEEL LESS ABOUT ANY MAN THAT DIDN'T FALL IN LOVE WITH YOU."

WELL... WOULD YOU LIKE TO GO OUT TO DINNER OR SOMETHING WITH ME?

I NEED TO TELL YOU, I WAS SURPRISED AND DELIGHTED THAT THIS HANDSOME MAN LOOKED ME IN THE EYES WHEN WE WERE TALKING. THAT'S A RARE THING FOR ME.

THERE WAS ONE THING HE WAS ALWAYS SURE ABOUT:

BETTER SET ANOTHER PLATE, MA, BECAUSE THIS IS THE GIRL I'M GONNA MARRY!

AND WE DID.

ON OUR 50TH WEDDING ANNIVERSARY, HE SAID:

MY FIRST THOUGHT WAS, "I'M GONNA MARRY THAT GIRL." MY SECOND THOUGHT WAS, "LORD SHE'S GOOD LOOKIN'." AND THAT WAS THE DAY MY LIFE BEGAN.

I WOULDN'T TRADE THE LAST FIFTY YEARS FOR NOTHING ON THIS EARTH.

HE'S JUST THE FUNNIEST, WITTIEST GUY IN THE WORLD AND HE'S REALLY BRIGHT. HE'S NOT BACKWARD AT ALL, HE JUST DOESN'T HAVE ANY DESIRE TO BE IN SHOW BUSINESS,

AND HE DOESN'T WANT PEOPLE TO HAVE HIS PICTURES IN THE PAPER.

IN MY WILDEST DREAMS, I DIDN'T EXPECT THINGS TO TAKE OFF LIKE THEY DID. IT REALLY STARTED WHEN I MET PORTER WAGONER.

I REMEMBER HUDDLING IN FRONT OF THE TELEVISION TO WATCH THE PORTER WAGONER SHOW.

PORTER, "THE THIN MAN FROM WEST PLAINS, MISSOURI," HAD 29 TOP-TEN HITS DURING HIS CAREER, INCLUDING "MISERY LOVES COMPANY" AND "THE COLD HARD FACTS OF LIFE."

THE WAGON HOUSE

SOME SAY I HELPED REIGNITE HIS SINGING AND SONGWRITING CAREER.

AT THE TIME, I WASN'T WORRIED ABOUT ALL THAT. HE PAID ME $60,000 A YEAR TO BE A VOCALIST ON HIS SHOW, AND I WAS ONLY 21 YEARS OLD. THAT'S GOOD MONEY. I PROMISED TO STAY WITH HIM FOR FIVE YEARS.

WE HAD 21 HITS TOP THE CHARTS TOGETHER AND WON THE COUNTRY MUSIC ASSOCIATION'S VOCAL DUO OF THE YEAR AWARD THREE TIMES.

BUT I ALWAYS SAY, "IF YOU DON'T LIKE THE ROAD YOU'RE WALKING ON, PAVE ANOTHER."

I KNEW IT WAS TIME TO BE ON MY OWN. I WANTED MORE. I WANTED HOLLYWOOD.

MY WEAKNESSES HAVE ALWAYS BEEN FOOD AND MEN — IN THAT ORDER.

PORTER HAD BEEN INSTRUMENTAL IN MY DEVELOPMENT AS AN ARTIST. I MEAN, I COULD SING WHEN I MET HIM, BUT HE TAUGHT ME HOW TO BE A PERFORMER. I HATED TO BREAK HIS HEART.

BUT IT WAS 1974, AND IT WAS TIME FOR ME TO GO. I KNEW IT. HE KNEW IT. IT WAS JUST DIFFICULT TO PUT INTO WORDS, YOU KNOW?

I Will Allways Love You

WAGONER

PORTER, PLEASE SIT DOWN. I'VE WRITTEN THIS SONG, AND I WANT YOU TO HEAR IT.

THE SONG IS SAYING, "JUST BECAUSE I'M GOING DON'T MEAN I WON'T LOVE YOU. I APPRECIATE YOU, AND I HOPE YOU DO GREAT, AND I APPRECIATE EVERYTHING YOU'VE DONE, BUT I'M OUT OF HERE."

IT WAS MY WAY TO SAY GOODBYE.

THAT'S THE PRETTIEST SONG I EVER HEARD. AND YOU CAN GO, PROVIDING I GET TO PRODUCE THAT RECORD.

AND HE DID.

AFTER PORTER, I TOURED A BIT WITH MY "TRAVELING FAMILY BAND." MY FAMILY HAD GROWN UP SINGING AND PLAYING MUSIC, SO WHY NOT?

THAT ENDED IN 1976. BY THEN, I'D CREATED A PUBLISHING COMPANY AND STARTED ENTERTAINING THE IDEA OF BEIN' A MOVIE STAR. MY VARIETY SHOW, DOLLY, WAS BORN.

LADIES AND GENTLEMEN! MISS DOLLY PARTON

THE SHOW OPENED EACH WEEK WITH A CLOSE-UP ON A BUTTERFLY MADE OF LIGHT PERCHED ATOP MY NAME. THE CAMERA WOULD PULL BACK, REVEALING MY NAME. I'D GLIDE INTO THE FRAME ON A VELVET ROPE SWING AS RALPH EMERY, OUR ANNOUNCER, SAID:

AND THEN I'D SING. IT WAS ALL VERY 1970'S.

THE SHOW WAS THE MOST EXPENSIVE SHOW EVER AIRED. IT COST $100,000 AN EPISODE AND ATTRACTED SINGERS LIKE EMMYLOU HARRIS, LINDA RONDSTADT, AND MARILYN MCCOO. IT WAS ALL REAL FANCY.

WE PULLED IN 9 MILLION VIEWERS A WEEK. NOT TOO SHABBY.

BUT IT WASN'T ENOUGH FOR ME. I PULLED THE PLUG AND THE STUDIO CITED IT AS "CREATIVE DIFFERENCES."

IN 1980, THINGS REALLY GOT CRAZY FOR ME.

NO, I CAN'T I'M JUST... TIRED, JANE.

LILY, PATRICIA RESNICK WROTE THE ROLE OF VIOLET NEWSTEAD WITH YOU IN MIND.

THEY'LL FIND SOMEONE ELSE. CAROL BURNETT OR SOMEONE. I'VE BEEN SHOOTING FOR SEVEN MONTHS –

THE INCREDIBLE SHRINKING WOMAN WAS –

A CHORE, JANE. I'VE MADE UP MY MIND.

THIS IS THE BIGGEST MISTAKE OF YOUR LIFE!

JANE WAGNER!

NOW YOU CALL TELL JANE FONDA AND TELL HER YOU'RE GOING TO TAKE THIS ROLE. I MEAN IT.

FINE, IF IT MEANS THAT MUCH TO YOU.

THE FILM STARS THREE WOMEN. I WONDER WHO THEY HAVE IN MIND FOR THE THIRD PERSON?

DOIN' 9 TO 5 WAS A GREAT DECISION, BOTH PERSONALLY AND PROFESSIONALLY. I MADE SOME LIFELONG FRIENDS, MADE A STATEMENT ABOUT WOMEN'S RIGHTS, AND RECEIVED AN OSCAR NOMINATION FOR WRITING THE TITLE SONG AND TWO GRAMMY AWARDS FOR BEST COUNTRY SONG AND BEST FEMALE COUNTRY VOCAL PERFORMANCE.

I KNOW WHO I AM; I KNOW WHAT I CAN AND CAN'T DO. I KNOW WHAT I WILL AND WON'T DO. I KNOW WHAT I AM CAPABLE OF AND I DON'T AGREE TO DO THINGS THAT I DON'T THINK I CAN PULL OFF.

SO IT WAS A NATURAL FIT FOR ME TO DO THE SCREEN VERSION OF BEST LITTLE WHOREHOUSE IN 1982.

NAYSAYERS THINK I'M SIMPLEMINDED BECAUSE I SEEM TO BE HAPPY. WHY SHOULDN'T I BE HAPPY? I HAVE EVERYTHING I EVER WANTED AND MORE. MAYBE I AM SIMPLEMINDED.

MAYBE THAT'S THE KEY: SIMPLE.

THAT REMINDS ME OF THE TIME I ALMOST QUIT MAKIN' MOVIES THANKS TO THE 1992 FILM, STRAIGHT TALK.

THE CHARACTER, SHIRLEE, WAS SO ME THAT I DIDN'T REALLY FEEL LIKE I WAS ACTING. BUT, OF COURSE, I HAD TO GO DEEP INSIDE AND I HAD A GREAT DIRECTOR.

IF I WAS TRYING TOO HARD TO DO IT MY WAY, HE WAS WONDERFUL TO SAY,

WELL, YOU NEED TO HAVE A LITTLE MORE EDGE.

BUT HE LIKED ME DOING MY OWN THING, BEING MY OWN SELF AS MUCH AS I COULD, SO I DIDN'T FEEL LIKE I WAS REALLY ACTING THAT MUCH. THAT WORRIED ME, OF COURSE.

IT WAS MY FIRST LEAD. I THINK I WAS TRYIN' TOO HARD. THE FILM RECEIVED LUKEWARM REVIEWS BUT DID HAVE SOME REDEEMING MOMENTS.

I PLAYED A RADIO HOST WHO SHOT STRAIGHT WITH MY ADVICE. IN ONE SCENE, A CALLER IS STRUGGLING WITH THE DECISION TO BECOME TRANSGENDER. I GOT TO SAY,

IF YOU'RE SURE THAT'S WHAT YOU REALLY WANT, ALL I CAN SAY IS DON'T TRY TO PERM YOUR OWN HAIR AND DON'T WEAR HIGH HEELS ON A SOGGY LAWN!

YOU RECENTLY THREW SUPPORT TO THE LGBT COMMUNITY...

OH, I'M ALWAYS ENCOURAGING – WELL, I'M NOT ENCOURAGING – THEY MADE ME THE POSTER CHILD I THINK BECAUSE I'M SO OUTSPOKEN AS BEING ACCEPTING OF PEOPLE IN GENERAL. WE ARE ALL GOD'S CHILDREN.

I'VE OFTEN SAID PEOPLE DON'T COME TO SEE ME TO SEE ME, THEY COME TO SEE ME TO SEE THEM.

I'VE FOUGHT FOR THE RIGHT TO BE MYSELF, SO THAT IS ONE OF THE REASONS THAT THE GAYS AND LESBIANS RELATE TO ME. THEY KNOW THAT I APPRECIATE EVERYBODY FOR WHO THEY ARE.

WE ARE WHO WE ARE, SO WHY CAN'T WE BE ALLOWED TO BE THAT? I DON'T WANT TO BE CONTROVERSIAL OR STIR UP A BUNCH OF TROUBLE BUT PEOPLE ARE GOING TO LOVE WHO THEY ARE GOING TO LOVE. I THINK GAY COUPLES SHOULD BE ALLOWED TO MARRY.

THEY SHOULD SUFFER JUST LIKE US HETEROSEXUALS.

I SAY, "YOU NEED TO LET PEOPLE KNOW WHO YOU ARE AND YOU NEED TO COME ON OUT. YOU DON'T NEED TO LIVE YOUR LIFE IN DARKNESS — WHAT'S THE POINT IN THAT?

"YOU'RE NEVER GONNA BE HAPPY; YOU'RE GONNA BE SICK. YOU'RE NOT GONNA BE HEALTHY IF YOU TRY TO SUPPRESS YOUR FEELINGS AND WHO YOU ARE."

I TRY TO SEE THE GOOD IN EVERYBODY, AND I DON'T CARE WHO PEOPLE ARE AS LONG AS THEY'RE THEMSELVES, WHATEVER THAT IT.

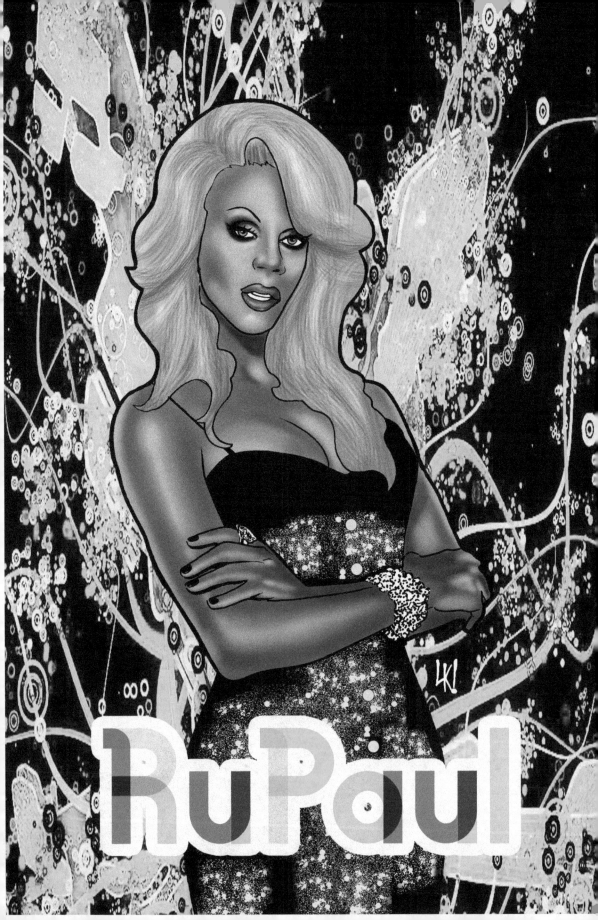

RuPaul

"WE ALL CAME INTO THIS WORLD NAKED. THE REST IS ALL DRAG."
--RUPAUL

RUPAUL ANDRE CHARLES WAS BORN IN SAN DIEGO, NOVEMEBER 17, 1960. (SORRY TO SPILL YOUR AGE GIRL, WE SHOULD ALL LOOK SO FIERCE!) LEGEND HAS IT HIS HAIRDRESSER LOUISIANA NATIVE MOTHER GOT THE "RU" IN RUPAUL FROM THE ROUX THAT IS USED AS A THICKENING AGENT IN GUMBO. THOUGH BORN ON THE LEFT COAST RUPAUL GREW UP MOSTLY IN ATLANTA, GA.

SO GRAB SOME SNACKS, HUNKER DOWN AND BE PREPARED. PREFERABLY NITROGLYCERIN AS THIS IS A TELANOVIA NOT FOR THE FAINT OF HEART. INSET OF TINY RUPAUL HEAD WITH CARMEN MIRANDA FRUIT BASKET ON HEAD.

AY CARAMBA!

RUPAUL GOT SOMETHING OF A BREAK WITH A CAMEO IN THE 1989 VIDEO SMASH HIT "LOVE SHACK" BY FELLOW ATLANTEAN'S THE B-52'S. SO HURRY UP AND GRAB YOUR JUKE BOX MONEY!

TIN ROOF... *RUSTED!!!*

RUPAUL STOOD OUT ADDING HIS BRAND OF COLOR TO THAT "FUNKY LITTLE SHACK."

BREAKING MORE GROUND FOR DRAG KIND, 1995 SAW THE AIRING OF THE SHORT LIVED YET EXTREMELY ENTERTAINING "RUPAUL SHOW" ON VH1. ONE VERY SPECIAL EPISODE RU'S GUEST WAS TV"S OWN WONDER WOMAN, LYNDA CARTER. MERCIFUL MINERVA! THAT MUST HAVE BEEN AN EPIC MEETING OF AMAZON AND GLAMAZON!

HI, EVERYBODY! DO YOU LIKE MY OUTFIT. THIS IS THE FRONT--

RUPAUL WAS EVER THE HOSTESS WITH THE MOSTEST WITH HIS HILARIOUS OPENING MONOLGUES AND WITTY BANTER WITH GUESTS.

AND THIS IS THE FRONT!

AND GIRLFRIEND SURE DOES KNOW HOW TO FILL OUT A FABULOUS GOWN!

YOU ARE ONE OF MY IDOLS AND I THINK YOU ARE JUST WONDER-FUL! ARE YOU SURE YOU WON'T DO IT FOR US?

I AM SO F LATTERED. BUT AS I TOLD YOU THE LASSO AND THE TWIRL ARE PERMANENTLY RETIRED.

CRANKY OLD MEN NOTWITHSTANDING, SUCCESS IS THE BEST REVENGE. IT'S NOT EVERY "GIRL" THAT GETS A DOLL MADE OF HER AFTER ALL. 200? SAW THE RELEASE OF THE GORGEOUSLY FABULOUS RUPAUL DOLL IN? DIFFERENT STYLES. FAIR WARNING TO A CERTAIN B-WORD" BLONDE DOLL WITH BLUE EYES, THERE'S A NEW DOLL ON THE BLOCK! (YOU BETTER WORK!)

WE ALWAYS KNEW YOU WERE A DOLL, RU. NOW YOU REALLY ARE! NOW WE JUST NEED THE SUIT WEARING RUPAUL CHARLES "KEN DOLL".

HAVING CONQUERED MUSIC AND TELEVISION, RUPAUL IS NO SLOUCH WHEN IT COMES TO THE SILVER SCREEN. AS EXPECTED SHE IS A NATURAL AND FUN TO WATCH. LOOK OUT MERYL!

RUPAUL WAS PROMINENTLY FEATURED IN THE 1985 DRAGUMENTARY WIGSTOCK THE FESTIVAL REMINISCENT OF WOODSTOCK, YOU KNOW THE HIPPY CONCERT. BUT THIS TIME WITH DRAG QUEENS. (AND PROBABLY A FEW MORE DIFFERENCES THAN THAT!)

RUPAUL ALSO PLAYED A SUPER MODEL THAT GOES UNDERCOVER AS A HOOKER TO RESCUE HER NIECE FROM AN EVIL BODY PARTS BROKER IN THE 2007 EPIC, STAR BOOTY. PROVING HE CAN LOOK FIERCE, KICK BUTT AND FIGHT CRIME ALL AT THE SAME TIME. AS IF WE EVER HAD ANY DOUBT THAT OUR LADY RU WOULD TURN THE MOTHER OUT.

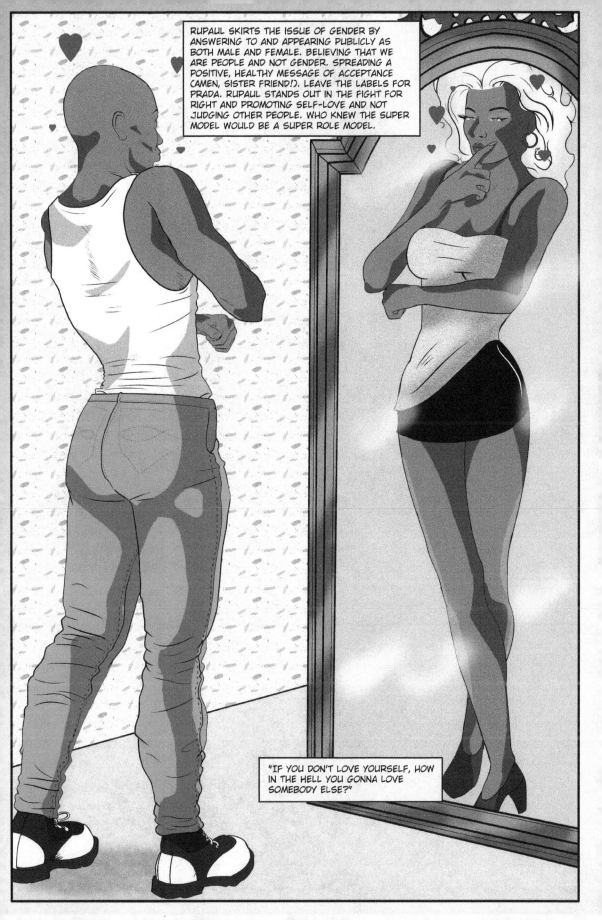

RUPAUL SKIRTS THE ISSUE OF GENDER BY ANSWERING TO AND APPEARING PUBLICLY AS BOTH MALE AND FEMALE. BELIEVING THAT WE ARE PEOPLE AND NOT GENDER. SPREADING A POSITIVE, HEALTHY MESSAGE OF ACCEPTANCE (AMEN, SISTER FRIEND!). LEAVE THE LABELS FOR PRADA. RUPAUL STANDS OUT IN THE FIGHT FOR RIGHT AND PROMOTING SELF-LOVE AND NOT JUDGING OTHER PEOPLE. WHO KNEW THE SUPER MODEL WOULD BE A SUPER ROLE MODEL.

"IF YOU DON'T LOVE YOURSELF, HOW IN THE HELL YOU GONNA LOVE SOMEBODY ELSE?"

What other people think of me is not my business. What I do is what I do. How people see me doesn't change what I decide to do. I don't choose projects so people don't see me as one thing or another. I choose projects that excite me. I think the problem is people refuse to understand what drag is outside of their belief system.

- Rupaul

WHO NEEDS GHANDI WHEN WE HAVE RUPAUL? JUST KIDDING "G", LOVE YOU LIKE A GURU- BUT MAKE MINE RURU!

CHER WAS BORN **CHERILYN SARKISIAN** ON MAY 20, 1946 IN EL CENTRO, CALIFORNIA.

HER PARENTS DIVORCED AND, WHEN MONEY BECAME TIGHT, THE YOUNG CHER WAS TEMPORARILY PLACED IN A FOSTER HOME.

THE INTROVERTED GIRL CAME ALIVE WHEN THE MOVIES SHE SAW TURNED HER IN THE DIRECTION OF MUSIC AND SONG.

SENSING A CREATIVE SPARK, CHER'S MOTHER MANAGED TO SCRAPE TOGETHER MONEY FOR ACTING LESSONS FOR HER DAUGHTER.

UNDIAGNOSED DYSLEXIA CONTRIBUTED TO CHER'S STRUGGLES IN SCHOOL AND TO HER DROPPING OUT OF FRESNO HIGH SCHOOL AT AGE 16. AND SHORTLY THEREAFTER...

...MADE HER WAY TO HOLLYWOOD WHERE SHE WAS SURE SHE WOULD FIND FAME AND FORTUNE.

CHER WAS INTRODUCED TO RECORD PRODUCER *SONNY BONO* WHO OFFERED HER HIS SPARE ROOM WITH NO STRINGS ATTACHED BECAUSE HE DID NOT FIND HER ATTRACTIVE. HE QUICKLY FOUND HER WORK...

...AS A SESSION SINGER ON SONGS BY THE *RIGHTEOUS BROTHERS*, DARLENE LOVE, THE RONETTES AND THE CRYSTALS.

SONNY PRODUCED AND WROTE TWO CHER SINGLES IN 1964, UNDER THE NAMES BONNIE JO MASON AND CHERILYN; BOTH OF WHICH FAILED TO HIT THE CHARTS.

THE RELATIONSHIP TURNED ROMANTIC AND THE COUPLE WERE MARRIED IN TIJUANA, MEXICO IN 1964.

THE COUPLE TOOK THE NEXT PROFESSIONAL STEP IN 1965 WITH THE RELEASE OF THE ALBUM, *"LOOK AT US"*, WHICH PRODUCED THE FIRST OF MANY CHART HITS, *"I GOT YOU BABE"*...

...AND APPEARANCES ON THE MOST POPULAR VARIETY SHOWS OF THE DAY LIKE *THE ED SULLIVAN SHOW.*

CHER WAS AN IMMEDIATE TRENDSETTER IN FASHION WITH HER OFTEN ECCENTRIC CLOTHING AND EXOTIC GOOD LOOKS.

EARLY BOUTS OF STAGE FRIGHT WERE OVERCOME BY REGULAR BETWEEN SONG JOKES AT THE EXPENSE OF SONNY.

CHER LAUNCHED A SOLO CAREER IN 1965-66 WITH THREE ALBUMS THAT PRODUCED SUCH HITS AS *"ALL I REALLY WANT TO DO"* AND *"BANG BANG (MY BABY SHOT ME DOWN)"*.

THE MUSICAL WINDS OF CHANGING WERE SHIFTING AND BY 1967, SONNY AND CHER WERE NO LONGER RELEVANT.

THE ATTEMPT TO BROADEN THEIR HORIZONS INTO FILM RESULTED IN THE BOX OFFICE BOMBS *"GOOD TIMES"* AND *"CHASTITY"*.

CHER BECAME PREGNANT MIDWAY THROUGH 1968 AND, ON MARCH 4, 1969, *CHASTITY BONO* WAS BROUGHT INTO THE WORLD.

THE MUSICAL/VARIETY/COMEDY SHOW, *"THE SONNY AND CHER COMEDY HOUR"*, BROUGHT THE DUO TO TELEVISION IN 1971.

CHER'S SOLO CAREER REEMERGED WITH HITS LIKE *"GYPSIES, TRAMPS & THIEVES"*, *"HALF-BREED"* AND *"DARK LADY"*.

THE PERSONAL AND PROFESSIONAL LIVES OF SONNY AND CHER ENDED IN 1974 WHEN THE COUPLE SEPARATED...

...EFFECTIVELY KILLING THEIR SHOW AND ENDING IN A BITTER DIVORCE THAT WOULD DRAG ON UNTIL 1979.

CHER MADE THE MOST OF NEWFOUND FREEDOM AND WAS REGULARLY ON THE ARM OF SUCH CELEBRITIES AS *ELVIS PRESLEY*, KISS'S *GENE SIMMONS*, RECORD COMPANY EXECUTIVE *DAVID GEFFEN* AND ALLMAN BROTHERS BAND FRONT MAN *GREG ALLMAN*.

THREE DAYS AFTER FINALIZING HER DIVORCE FROM SONNY, CHER AND GREG ALLMAN WERE MARRIED ON JUNE 30, 1975.

THE MARRIAGE PRODUCED A SON, *ELIJAH BLUE ALLMAN*, BORN IN JULY 1976...

...AN ALBUM ENTITLED *"TWO THE HARD WAY"* BY ALLMAN AND WOMAN THAT BOMBED...

...AND A MARRIAGE THAT WOULD END TWO YEARS AFTER IT BEGAN. CHER WAS ONCE AGAIN ON HER OWN.

CHER CAUGHT THE TAIL END OF THE DISCO CRAZE IN 1979 WITH THE TOP TEN HIT *"TAKE ME HOME"*.

CHER TOOK A STAB AT ROCK AND ROLL THE FOLLOWING YEAR BUT HER BLACK ROSE BAND PERSONA FELL ON DEAF EARS.

BUT BY 1982 CHER'S MUSIC CAREER WAS ONCE AGAIN ON THE SKIDS. SHE WAS AT A LOSS AS TO WHAT TO DO NEXT.

THAT'S WHEN SHE DECIDED THAT DESPITE BEING IN HER MID 30'S AND HAVING VERY LITTLE EXPERIENCE...

...SHE WOULD TURN TO ACTING.

CTOR

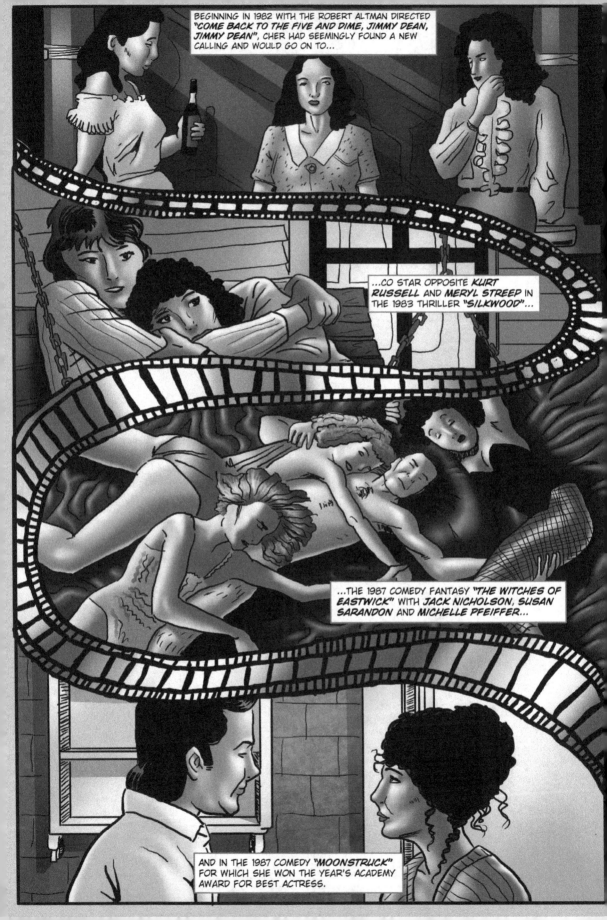

BEGINNING IN 1982 WITH THE ROBERT ALTMAN DIRECTED "*COME BACK TO THE FIVE AND DIME, JIMMY DEAN, JIMMY DEAN*", CHER HAD SEEMINGLY FOUND A NEW CALLING AND WOULD GO ON TO...

...CO STAR OPPOSITE *KURT RUSSELL* AND *MERYL STREEP* IN THE 1983 THRILLER "*SILKWOOD*"...

...THE 1987 COMEDY FANTASY "*THE WITCHES OF EASTWICK*" WITH *JACK NICHOLSON*, *SUSAN SARANDON* AND *MICHELLE PFEIFFER*...

AND IN THE 1987 COMEDY "*MOONSTRUCK*" FOR WHICH SHE WON THE YEAR'S ACADEMY AWARD FOR BEST ACTRESS.

CHER'S STAR STUDDED ROMANTIC LIFE DURING THIS PERIOD INCLUDED ACTORS *TOM CRUISE* AND *VAL KILMER* AND THE ROB CAMILLETTI, A 22 YEAR OLD BAGEL MAKER, WHO SHE MET SHORTLY AFTER TURNING 40 AND LIVED WITH FOR THREE YEARS.

CHER RECAPTURED MUSICAL SUCCESS BETWEEN 1987-1990 WITH SUCH HITS AS *"IF I COULD TURN BACK TIME"* AND *"I FOUND SOMEONE"*. A LIVE VEGAS CONCERT WAS FILMED AND WAS A TV RATINGS WINNER WHEN RELEASED AS *"CHER-LIVE AT THE MIRAGE"*.

CHER'S KARMA CHANGED FOLLOWING THE DEATH OF SONNY AND LAUNCHED HER INTO A FOUR YEAR PERIOD OF CREATIVE AND COMMERCIAL SUCCESS.

THE ALBUM *"BELIEVE"* WAS A WORLDWIDE SMASH IN 1998 AND RESULTED IN A GRAMMY AWARD FOR THE TITLE TRACK.

THAT SAME YEAR CHER'S MEMOIR, *"THE FIRST TIME"*, WAS PUBLISHED AND BECAME AN INTERNATIONAL BEST SELLER.

WHEN RECORD COMPANIES REJECTED AN ALBUM OF CHER WRITTEN SONGS, SHE TOOK THE BULL BY THE HORNS AND RELEASED "NOT.COM.MERCIAL" ONLINE TO CRITICAL AND COMMERCIAL RAVES.

BETWEEN 2000 AND 2002, CHER HAD SOME MINOR HITS, PRIMARILY OVERSEAS...

...CAPTURED TWO GRAMMY NOMINATIONS AND A BILLBOARD AWARD.

BUT THE GRIND OF STARDOM WAS TAKING ITS TOLL AND SO IN MAY 2002...

... SHE ANNOUNCED THAT THE UPCOMING LIVING PROOF: THE FAREWELL TOUR WOULD BE HER LAST.

THE FAREWELL TOUR, FEATURING ELABORATE COSTUMES, A FULL BAND AND AERIAL ACROBATS, WAS A WORLDWIDE SENSATION DURING ITS 2003-2005 RUN. IF CHER WERE TRULY GOING OUT, SHE WAS GOING OUT WITH A BANG.

IN 2008, THE NOW 61 YEAR OLD CHER SIGNED A MULTI-MILLION DOLLAR, THREE YEAR DEAL TO PERFORM 200 SHOWS AT *CEASAR'S PALACE*.

ON THE ROMANCE FRONT, CHER MADE HEADLINES IN 2009 BY DATING 38 YEAR OLD BIKER TIM MEDVETZ...

...AND AMERICAN COMEDY WRITER RON ZIMMERMAN IN 2010.

NOW WELL INTO HER 60'S, CHER IS SHOWING NO SIGNS OF SLOWING DOWN.

CHER RECORDED ANOTHER ALBUM WHICH IS SCHEDULED FOR A 2011 RELEASE.

SHE STARED IN THE SUCCESSFUL FILM "*BURLESQUE*" WITH *CHRISTINA AGUILERA*.

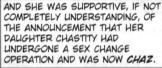

AND SHE WAS SUPPORTIVE, IF NOT COMPLETELY UNDERSTANDING, OF THE ANNOUNCEMENT THAT HER DAUGHTER CHASTITY HAD UNDERGONE A SEX CHANGE OPERATION AND WAS NOW *CHAZ*.

She was born *Stefani Joanne Angelina Germanotta* on *March 28, 1986* to parents *Cynthia Bissett* and *Joseph Germanotta*.

Music, obviously, was a huge part of her childhood. She learned piano at age four...

She even wrote her first ballad at 13 years old. How many of us can say that they accomplished something like that at age 13?

She attended a private Catholic school in Manhattan but has been very adamant that she wasn't wealthy as a child, instead talking of how her family worked for everything they wanted or needed.

She sang at open mike nights while still very young...

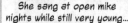

She was an actress in high school, and well known for her acting abilities. It is something we can definitely see today in the *Gaga* persona.

But high school wasn't all fun and games. She was different and people made her feel like a freak for who she was. At least, that's how she felt. Others might not agree with that history, but to *Gaga*, that's the truth.

Things changed from then on.

At 17, she was admitted to NYU and the Tisch School of the Arts, a feat that proves her dedication to her craft and her abilities.

She studied music and her songwriting became more advanced...

She worked hard, and felt like she was more creative than others, that she wanted it more. But school stopped appealing to her and she withdrew...

Soon, she became *Lady Gaga*. There are conflicting reports on how the name came to be, but one of the most prevalent, and interesting, is that she loved the song *Radio Ga Ga* by *Queen* and because of an autocorrect error on a text from her producer, she became *Lady Gaga*. And that was that. Such a better story than just some marketing meeting, right?

Before striking it big on the music scene, she performed in New York's club scene with *Lady Starlight* as performance art with the *Lady Gaga* and the *Starlight Revue*.

PIANOS

...And began to focus on her musical career. But she made a *promise* to her father.

She and *Starlight* played *Lollapalooza* in 2007 and the crowd went wild.

Fusari, her recording partner who helped her come up with the name *Lady Gaga*, sent the songs they worked on to another producer and record executive. From there...

...She was quickly signed to a record deal with *Streamline Records*, part of *Interscope*. This was it. Here she was. *Lady Gaga* had arrived.

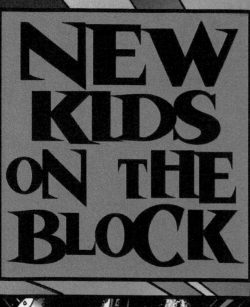

She struck a deal writing songs for people like *Britney Spears*, *New Kids on the Block* and others. She was writing her own songs as well, and starting to make a name for herself. Pretty soon, everywhere you looked, *there* would be *Lady Gaga*.

She became one of the *go to* writers in pop music, working all over the industry and continuing on her own stuff as well.

Her own music became *The Fame*, released in 2008 to critical praise and acclaim from the public as well.

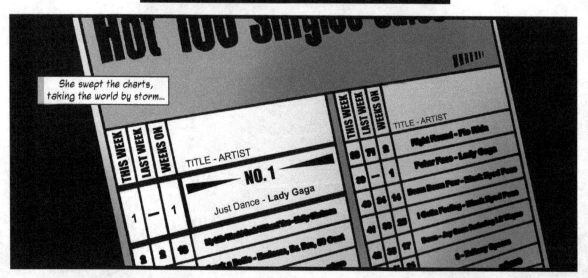

She swept the charts, taking the world by storm...

Her first single, *Just Dance*, became not only a chart-topper, but a hit music video and a phenomenon of its own.

And it was a huge song, up until her second single dropped...

...*Poker Face*. She was noticed almost immediately all over the world, and her album was playing everywhere she went.

The song would go on to win her Grammys for Song of the Year, Record of the Year, Best Electronic/Dance Album and just swept the world.

She was all over the place, and to most, seemed to have popped up over night. It was surprising, and her newfound *Fame*...

...Allowed her fashion sense to be noticed by people and not questioned. She was a pop superstar, winning *MTV Video Music Awards*, topping the charts all over the world, and finding her own niche...

...She could wear whatever she wanted, and people would talk about it. It was part of her persona as *Lady Gaga*, and we were all along for the ride.

She dropped her album the *Fame Monster* and went on tour in its support, and even released another hit single, *Bad Romance*. She rocketed to the top...

...Even performing for the *Queen*!

Beyond the music, she is not just some flash-in-the-pan superstar. She has a message. She has appeared on the *Ellen Degeneres Show*, praising Ellen for being an inspiration to both women and the gay community. Gaga is very outspoken about her support of gay rights...

...And equality for everyone.

But it was her music and her fashion sense that first got her noticed, and gave her the ability to speak out and speak her mind.

And in her vocalizing about herself and her thoughts on the world, she's been open about her musical influences, from *Queen* down the line to *Britney Spears*. She's a superstar who is very open about who she is and where she's come from...

...And even enjoys when comparisons are made between her and other superstars like *Christina Aguilera*. She doesn't hide from them, she takes them head-on, just like the critics...

...And like the rumors or urban legends. When asked by *Barbara Walters* about her androgyny and the possibility of her being intersex, she took it head on, dismissing the claim and acknowledging that she revels in the androgyny on-stage and again, revels in the questions.

Like I said, she's all over the place, and this is just the tip of the iceberg.

THE
100
MOST
INFLUENTIAL
PEOPLE
IN THE
WORLD

She took the world by storm and she's now not only seen all over the news media and in magazines and newspaper articles, but on television too.

She's been on *Saturday Night Live* and there's even been an episode of *Glee* devoted to her music.

But no matter what she does, whether it be collaborations with *Beyonce* or her outlandish outfits or just going on television, we can't stop talking about her.

LARRY KING LIVE

Entertainment WEEKLY

It's part of the *Fame Monster* she's talked about and sung about. We constantly want to know what she's doing...

...And the news media follows her everywhere.

We dissect her clothing more than her music, and even argue about the outfits on television, determining if she's a fashion icon as well as a music icon.

It's all part of the *Lady Gaga* persona.

As is the *Haus of Gaga*, not to be confused with the *House of Gaga*, her own music publishing company. *The Haus* is her collective of artists, performers and back-stage presence that help her become *Lady Gaga*.

They build the sets, do the make-up, make the films that play during the performances; they all play a role in the persona of *Gaga*. Made up of close friends and new friends, they have all contributed to who Stefani is today.

She's taken the world by storm. She's a superstar. And all we hear is *Lady Gaga*. In spite of that, in spite of her being everywhere, people just can't seem to get enough of her. And that will be her true claim to *Fame*: her staying power.

THE END

TIDALWAVE
COMICS

Sandra C. Ruckdeschel, Dan Rafter, Spike Steffenhagen, CW Cooke, Kimberly Sherman — **Writers**

Pedro Ponzo, Kristopher Smith, Aaron Sowd, Beniamino Bradi, Warren Martineck — **Artist**

Benjamin Glibert & Warren Montgomery — **Letters**

Darren G. Davis — **Editor**

George Amaru — **Cover**

Darren G. Davis
Publisher

Maggie Jessup
Publicity

Susan Ferris
Entertainment Manager

Steven Diggs Jr.
Marketing Manager

Divider Images by: Randy Green, Michal Szyksznian, Vinnie Tartamella and Beniamino Bradi

CPSIA information can be obtained
at www.ICGtesting.com
Printed in the USA
BVHW061958080621
609009BV00007B/573